Kids Learn!

Getting Ready for

1st Grade

Contributing Author

Jodene Smith, M.A.Ed.

Publishing Credits

Conni Medina, M.A.Ed., *Managing Editor*; Robin Erickson, *Production Director*;
Lee Aucoin, *Creative Director*; Timothy J. Bradley, *Illustration Manager*;
Aubrie Nielsen, M.S.Ed., *Senior Editor*; Caroline Gasca, M.S.Ed., *Editor*;
Melina Sánchez, *Assistant Editor*; Marissa Rodriguez, *Designer*;
Stephanie Reid, *Photo Editor*; Rachelle Cracchiolo, M.S.Ed., *Publisher*

Image Credits

p.8 Alamy; All other images Shutterstock.

Teacher Created Materials

5301 Oceanus Drive
Huntington Beach, CA 92649-1030
http://www.tcmpub.com
ISBN 978-1-4333-6788-5
© 2014 Teacher Created Materials, Inc.

Table of Contents

Introduction

Weekly Activities for Students

Appendices

Welcome to Kids Learn!

Dear Family,

Welcome to *Kids Learn! Getting Ready for 1st Grade*. First grade will be an exciting year, with plenty of new learning opportunities for your child. Your child will learn how to write complete sentences, add and subtract numbers, and count to 100! Interesting new topics in science and social studies will keep students engaged in lessons at school as well.

Kids Learn! was designed to help solidify the concepts your child learned in kindergarten and help your child prepare for the year ahead. The activities are based on college and career readiness standards and provide practice with essential skills for the grade level. Keeping the skills your child learned in kindergarten sharp while on break from school will help his or her first grade year get off to a great start.

Keep these tips in mind as you work with your child through the *Kids Learn!* book:

- Set aside **a specific time each day** to work on the activities.

- **Complete one language arts and one mathematics page** each time your child works in the book rather than an entire week's worth of activity pages at one time.

- Keep all **practice sessions with your child positive and constructive.** If the mood becomes tense or if either of you gets frustrated, set the book aside and find another time for your child to practice.

- **Help your child understand each activity** and provide guidance as he or she works through each page.

- Discuss the activities with your child. **Look for the** *Talk About It!* icon at the end of each activity.

- Encourage your child to do his or her best work and **compliment the effort that goes into learning.** Celebrate the completion of the activities by filling in the certificate at the end of the book and displaying it in a special place.

Enjoy the time learning with your child during his or her vacation from school. First grade will be here before you know it!

Top 10 Things Your First Grader Will Need to Know

1. **Read grade-level books** with ease and understanding

2. **Read and spell** sight words

3. **Write complete sentences** with correct capitalization and punctuation

4. **Count**, read, and write to 100

5. **Addition and subtraction** facts up to 20

6. Simple two-digit **addition and subtraction** problems (without regrouping)

7. Use the **five senses** (sight, taste, touch, sound, and smell) to observe and describe things

8. **Living things** and their habitats

9. **Rules and responsibilities** of being a good citizen

10. **The United States' holidays and symbols**

Sight Words 1–100

the	his	were	up	has	called
of	they	we	other	look	who
and	I	when	about	two	oil
a	at	your	out	more	sit
to	be	can	many	write	now
in	this	said	then	go	find
is	have	there	them	see	long
you	from	use	these	number	down
that	or	an	so	no	day
it	one	each	some	way	did
he	had	which	her	could	get
was	by	she	would	people	come
for	words	do	make	my	made
on	but	how	like	than	may
are	not	their	him	first	part
as	what	if	into	water	
with	all	will	time	been	

Things to Do at Home

To Develop Healthy Habits

- Make sure your child gets plenty of sleep by maintaining the same bedtime each night and keeping the room quiet to ensure a good night's rest. Children this age need 10–11 hours of sleep each night.

- Set aside a consistent time for homework each day. Designate a quiet area for your child to work and provide assistance when needed.

- Eat dinner as a family. During the meal, ask your child questions about his or her day and make sure to share stories from your own day, too!

SCHEDULE

4:00	Snack
4:30	Piano practice
5:00	Set the table, feed the dog
5:30	Dinner
6:30	Homework and reading time
7:15	Free time (after homework)
7:45	Get ready for bed

To Practice Reading

- Set aside a regular time of 15–20 minutes for reading or looking at picture books with your child. Discuss the story as well as the illustrations with your child and make sure to stop and ask questions while reading.

- Write the words to a story your child makes up on a sheet of paper. Have your child practice reading the story back to you.

- Encourage your child to help you follow the directions on a package of food. Items such as rice, macaroni and cheese, and cake mixes often provide pictures that can serve as visual cues to help your child read the words on the package.

Things to Do at Home (cont.)

To Practice Writing

- Put shaving cream, hair gel, or pudding in a plastic zipper bag and squeeze out as much air as possible. Place the bag on a flat surface. Have your child practice writing the letters of the alphabet on the bag with his or her index finger.

- Help your child select a photograph that he or she is in. Have your child write about what he or she is doing in the photograph.

- Help your child write a list of all the foods he or she has eaten that day.

To Practice Math

- Have your child gather 8–10 items from around your home. Sort the items in some way—for example, by color, shape, texture, or size.

- Use masking tape or sticky notes to label the bottom of each cup in a muffin tin with a number between 19 and 30. Give your child a collection of small objects such as beans, pasta, or buttons and ask him or her to count the correct number of items into each cup.

- Create visual math problems with household items. For example, use raisins to act out the following story problem: *If I start with six raisins and eat four of them, how many do I have left?*

Things to Do in the Community

To Develop Good Citizenship

- Help your child to think of a local citizen who contributes to the community in a positive way. Ask your child to draw a picture thanking him or her and deliver it in person.

- Read a book about composting together and discuss why composting is beneficial to the earth. Help your child start his or her own compost bucket and use the contents in a home or community garden.

- Discuss the importance of rules and laws with your child. Together, imagine a world with no rules and have your child illustrate some of the consequences.

To Practice Reading

- Select a letter of the alphabet before you leave the house to do errands. Have your child look for things in the community that start with that letter.

- Ask your child to try to read the signs at the grocery store. Seeing the food items above or below the sign can provide helpful visual clues to the written words.

- Go to your local library and check out a book on an unusual animal. Ask your child questions about the book as you read and have your child summarize parts of the book when you are finished.

Things to Do in the Community *(cont.)*

To Practice Writing

- Help your child write about what happened at the beginning, middle, and end of an outing you took in the community. Encourage your child to illustrate the events as well.

- Take your child to a new park. Help him or her draw a map of the park and label the playground equipment, landmarks, drinking fountains, and other noticeable features.

- Have your child take a small notepad or notebook along on an outing. Encourage him or her to write down words from the community and practice reading them when you return home.

To Practice Math

- Have your child look for numbers around the community. If possible, ask your child to count up to the number he or she identified.

- Go on a shape walk. Help your child identify objects that are squares, circles, triangles, cones, spheres, cubes, and cylinders. What other shapes can you find?

- Have your child identify objects in the community that are taller and shorter than he or she is. Extend the activity to objects that are heavier or lighter than your child.

Suggested Vacation Reading

These books are recommended for students in kindergarten and first grades. Most, if not all, of these books are available at your local library or bookstore. Encourage your child to read daily and record his or her reading progress on the Vacation Reading Log on page 11.

Fiction

Diary of a Wombat by Jackie French
Danny and the Dinosaur by Syd Hoff
My Friend Is Sad by Mo Willems
The Best Nest by P. D. Eastman
Extra Yarn by Mac Barnett
A Sick Day for Amos McGee by Philip C. Stead
The Sleepy Little Alphabet by Judy Sierra
Blueberries for Sal by Robert McCloskey
Quick as a Cricket by Audrey Wood
Toot & Puddle by Holly Hobbie

• •

Nonfiction

Animal Eyes by Dona Herweck Rice
Balloons Over Broadway: The True Story of the Puppeteer of Macy's Parade by Melissa Sweet
Step Gently Out by Helen Frost and Rick Lieder
All the Water in the World by George Ella Lyon
A Walk in London by Salvatore Rubbino
A Book About Color: A Clear and Simple Guide for Young Artists by Mark Gonyea
Dave the Potter: Artist, Poet, Slave by Laban Carrick Hill
Life-Size Aquarium by Teruyuki Komiya
Me, Frida by Amy Novesky
Who Will Plant a Tree? by Jerry Pallotta

#17788—Kids Learn: Getting Ready for 1st Grade

Vacation Reading Log

Help your child complete this reading log to keep track of his or her vacation reading.

Date	Title	Number of pages

Websites and Apps for Parents and Kids

Language Arts Websites

Reading Rockets: http://www.readingrockets.org
Information, activities, and advice for parents

Magic Keys: http://www.magickeys.com/books
Collection of online children's storybooks divided into sections for young children, older children, and young adults

ReadWriteThink: http://www.readwritethink.org/parent-afterschool-resources
Student materials that support literacy learning in the K–12 classroom

International Children's Digital Library: http://en.childrenslibrary.org
Online database of eBooks organized by age, reading level, language, genre, or interest

Starfall: http://www.starfall.com
Phonics program that introduces letter names and sounds and also contains a series of interactive reading material for beginning readers

Mathematics Websites

PBS Early Math: http://www.pbs.org/parents/education/math/milestones/first-second-grade
Math-based activities and developmental milestones for children from 6 to 9 years old

Sheppard Software: http://www.sheppardsoftware.com/math.htm
Collection of interactive math games covering a large variety of topics

SoftSchools.com: http://www.softschools.com/math
Math concepts, tips, games, and activity sheets

Figure This! Math Challenges for Families: http://www.figurethis.org
Math problems to challenge families

Education.com: http://www.education.com/activity/math
Suggestions for math games to make and play at home

Fun Educational Apps

Kids Learn Sight Words: 1–300
Teacher Created Materials, Inc.
Allows emerging readers to practice speaking, reading, and writing sight words

LetterSchool
Boreaal
Fun and engaging handwriting practice

Math Easy HD
Xiaofeng Ma
Ten math-based puzzles bridge the gap between counting and basic arithmetic

Bugs and Bubbles
Little Bit Studio, LLC
18 leveled activities provide practice with grade-level content and fine-motor skills

Weekly Activities for Students

© Teacher Created Materials

#17788—Kids Learn! Getting Ready for 1st Grade

13

Making New Words

Directions: Make new words by changing the first letter. Use the letter at the beginning of each row.

<u>s</u>un

<u>f</u>an

1. b _un_

2. r _____

3. f _____

4. m _____

5. r _____

6. c _____

Talk About It!

Which letters change? Say the sound of each letter.

#17788—Kids Learn! Getting Ready for 1st Grade

Shape Match

Directions: Draw a line from each shape to its name.

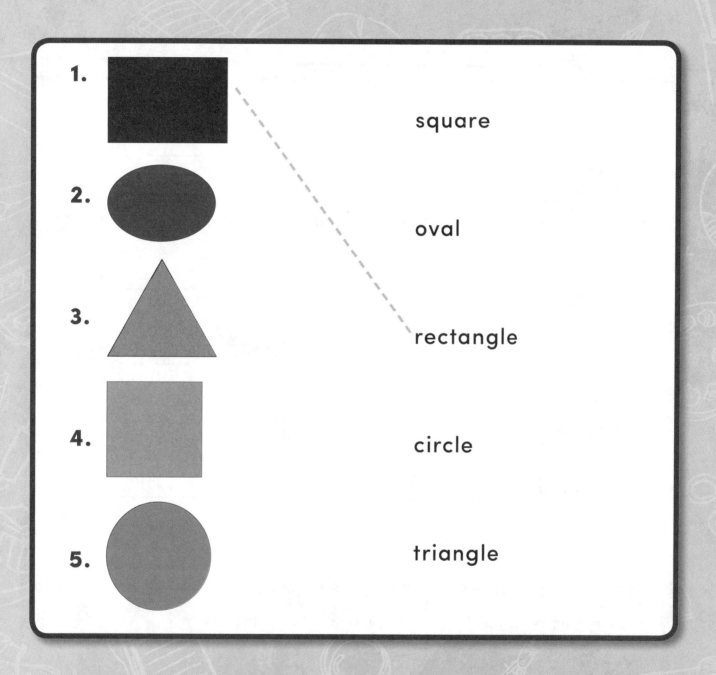

1. square

2. oval

3. rectangle

4. circle

5. triangle

Talk About It! What is the difference between a square and a rectangle?

Complete the Word

Directions: Write the missing letter to spell the word.

1. b ee

2. ___ og

3. ___ ill

4. ___ ing

5. ___ ut

6. ___ et

Talk About It! What sound does each letter you wrote make?

Light as a Feather

Directions: Circle the lighter object in each box.

1.

2.

3.

4.

5.

6.

Talk About It!

Which object is the heaviest?

The Mouse Ran Up the Clock

Directions: Connect the dots in alphabetical order.

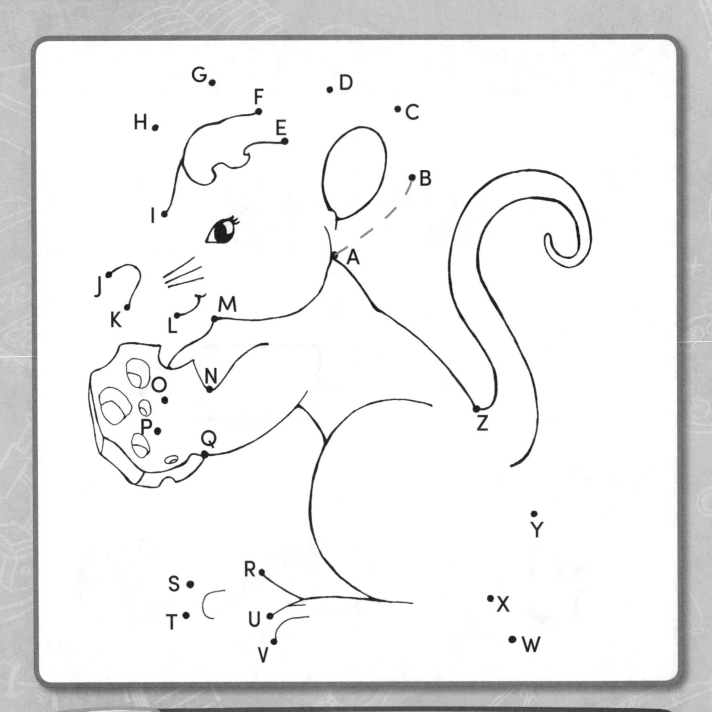

How do you know which letter comes next?

Gone Fishing

Directions: Count the fish in each set. Write the number on the line. Add the sets to find each total.

1.
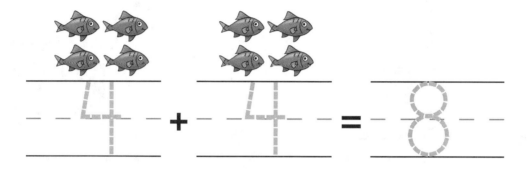

$$4 + 4 = 8$$

2.
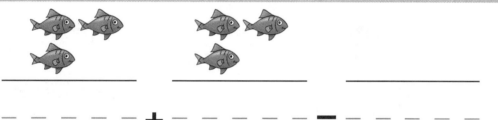

___ + ___ = ___

3.
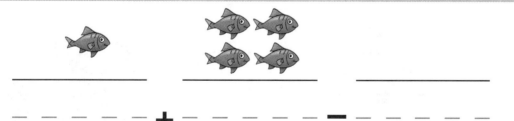

___ + ___ = ___

Talk About It! Is the total larger or smaller than the numbers you added? Why?

Starting Sounds

Directions: Say the name for each picture. Fill in the bubble for the letter that makes the beginning sound.

1.
- (A) k
- (B) t
- (C) b

2.
- (A) c
- (B) f
- (C) d

3.
- (A) f
- (B) j
- (C) r

4.
- (A) x
- (B) y
- (C) z

5.
- (A) m
- (B) n
- (C) b

6.
- (A) d
- (B) s
- (C) b

Talk About It!

What is the beginning sound in your name? What letter makes that sound?

Count Those Numbers

Directions: Count by one from the first number. Write each number you count.

1. 8, _____, _____, _____, _____, _____

2. 13, _____, _____, _____, _____, _____

3. 6, _____, _____, _____, _____, _____

4. 15, _____, _____, _____, _____, _____

5. 11, _____, _____, _____, _____, _____

6. 2, _____, _____, _____, _____, _____

Talk About It!

Which is the largest number you wrote? How do you know?

Word Riddles

Directions: Read each riddle. Circle the answer.

1. It has five fingers.
What is it?

band   (hand)

2. It is on a fish.
What is it?

fun   fin

3. I sleep on it.
What is it?

bell   bed

4. It goes quack.
What is it?

duck   luck

5. It can hit a ball.
What is it?

bet   bat

6. It can lay an egg.
What is it?

hen pen

Talk About It!

Make up a riddle for the word *rock*.

More Melons

Directions: Follow the steps for each problem.

1. How many melons?

Draw 1 more.
How many are there now?

_____

_ _ _ _

_____

3. How many melons?

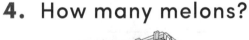

Draw 1 more.
How many are there now?

_____

_ _ _ _

_____

2. How many melons?

Draw 1 more.
How many are there now?

_____

_ _ _ _

_____

4. How many melons?

Draw 1 more.
How many are there now?

_____

_ _ _ _

_____

Does each number get larger or smaller? How do you know?

Animal Homes

Directions: Draw a picture and write a sentence about where each animal lives.

Which Ending?

Directions: Say the name of each picture. Write the last letter for each word.

1.  je __t__

2. ne _____

3. we_____

4. pe _____

5.  he _____

6. **10** te _____

What is the last sound in your name? What letter makes that sound?

Plane or Solid?

Directions: Write *s* next to the solid figures.
Write *p* next to the plane (flat) figures.

These are *plane* figures:

 triangle

 square
 rectangle
 circle

These are *solid* figures:

 cube
 prism
sphere
cone

1. 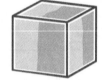 _____ s _____

2.  _____

3.  _____

4. _____

5. _____

6.  _____

Talk About It! Name a real object that is a sphere.

Use Tricky Words

Directions: Choose the right word from the Word Bank to complete the sentence.

Word Bank

for	not	that	was

1. The ball _____ was _____ in the box.

2. The bow is _____ me.

3. An ant is _____ big.

4. What is in _____ tub?

 Read aloud and spell the words in the Word Bank.

© Teacher Created Materials   #17788—Kids Learn! Getting Ready for 1st Grade   **27**

Longest and Shortest

Directions: Circle the correct picture.

1. Which is the longest?

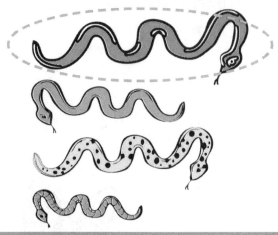

3. Which is the shortest?

2. Which is the shortest?

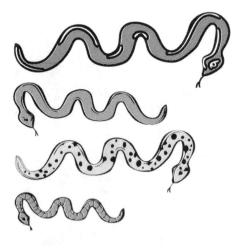

4. Which is the longest?

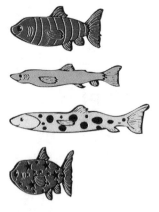

Which is the longest animal on this page? Which is the shortest?

#17788—*Kids Learn! Getting Ready for 1st Grade*

Capital Mistakes

Directions: Put a check by each sentence with a capital letter mistake.

1. I have a dog. ☐

   i have a dog. ☐

2. My dog has spots. ☐

   my dog has spots. ☐

3. May i pet your dog? ☐

   May I pet your dog? ☐

4. your dog is big! ☐

   Your dog is big! ☐

Talk About It!

Which word in a sentence always begins with a capital letter?

Subtraction Action

Directions: Solve each problem.

1. Cross out 4 sandwiches. How many are left?

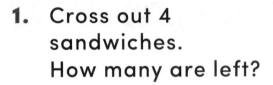

2. Cross out 2 peanuts. How many are left?

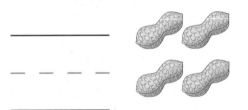

3. Cross out 1 pineapple. How many are left?

4. Cross out 5 worms. How many are left?

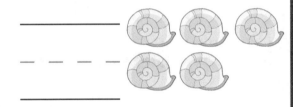

5. Cross out 3 shells. How many are left?

6. Cross out 0 clocks. How many are left?

Talk About It!

How did you know how many were left?

Find the Rhyme

Directions: Say the name of the picture in the box. Circle the picture that rhymes.

1.
2.
3.
4.

Talk About It!

Name a word that rhymes with *book*.

More or Less?

Directions: Draw a circle around the number that is more. Put an X on the number that is less.

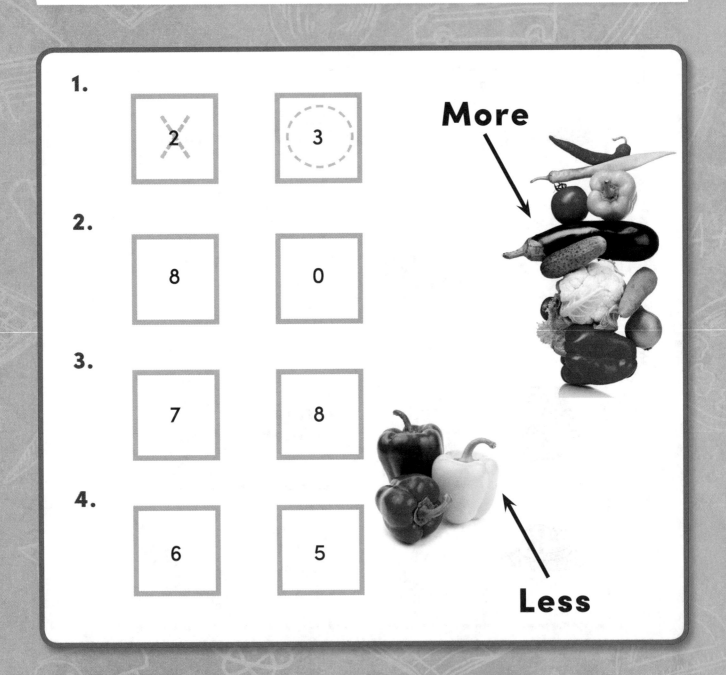

1. ⊠ 2   ⊙ 3   **More**

2. 8   0

3. 7   8

4. 6   5

Less

Short Vowel Stories

Directions: Read each sentence. Fill in the bubble beside the sentence that tells about the picture.

1.
- ○ The pig is in the pen.
- ○ The pig is on the mat.

2.
- ○ The frog is in a pot.
- ○ The frog is on the lily pad.

3.
- ○ The bug is in the net.
- ○ The bug sat on a rock.

4.
- ○ The dog sat in the sun.
- ○ The dog ran in the sun.

Talk About It!

Reread the sentences in number 4. Which word is different?

How Many Shoes?

Directions: Count the shoes. Then, write how many.

1.

How many shoes? _____

2.

How many shoes? _____

3.

How many shoes? _____

4.

How many shoes? _____

Talk About It!

Which problem shows 4 pairs of shoes?

The Best Day

Directions: Draw and write about your best day.

Making Rhyming Words

Directions: Write the word for each picture. Then, write a word that rhymes with it. *Hint:* Change the beginning letter.

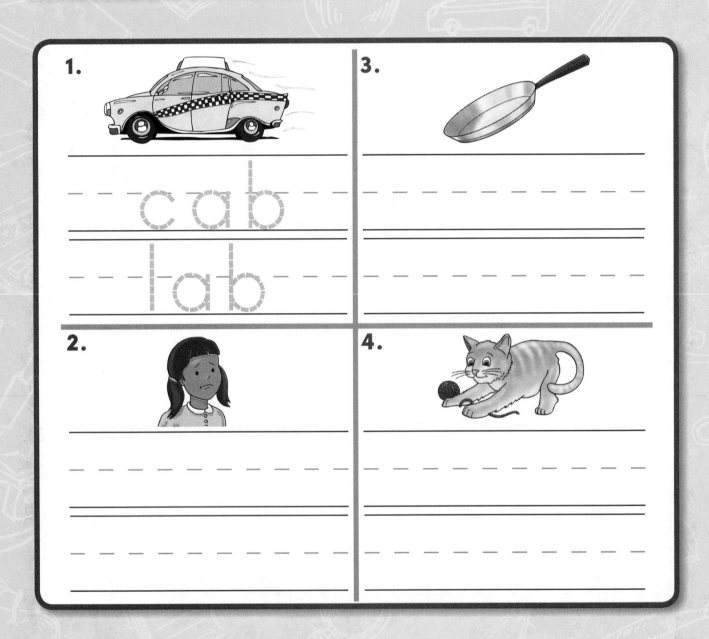

1. cab
   lab

3.

2.

4.

Talk About It! Which letter(s) did you change to make rhyming words?

Rectangle Robot

Directions: Color all the rectangles red. Color all the other shapes blue.

How can you recognize a rectangle?

#17788—Kids Learn! Getting Ready for 1st Grade

Short Vowel

Directions: Write the name for each picture. Use words from the Word Bank.

Word Bank

lip	pin	six	swim	bib	pig

1.

pig

2.

6

3.

4.

5.

6.

Talk About It!

Which vowel is in each word? What sound does it make?

The Surprise

Directions: Connect the dots in numerical order.

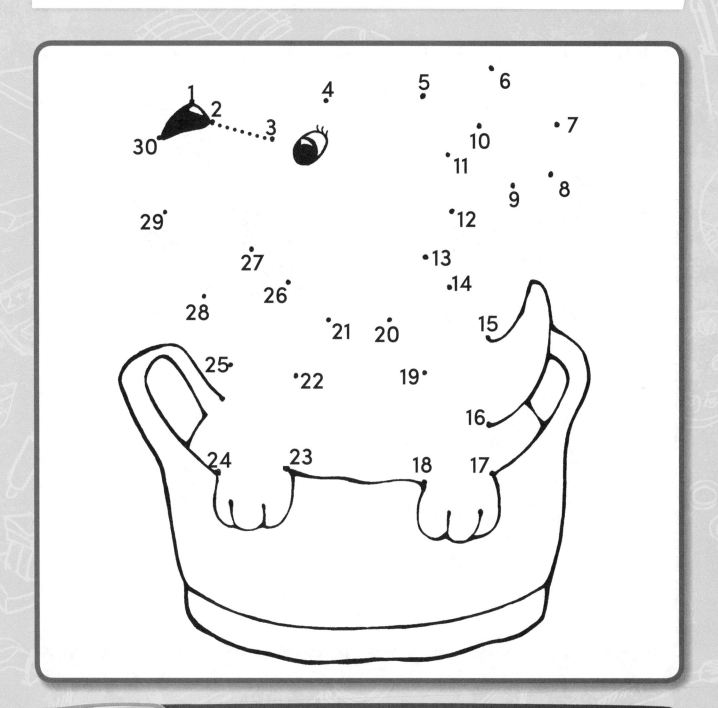

Talk About It!

How do you know which number comes next?

One or More?

Directions: Circle the word for each picture.

1.

pig   pigs

2.

pan   pans

3.

hat   hats

4.

sun   suns

Which letter at the end of a word shows more than one?

Take Away Some Bats

Directions: Count the bats. Then, follow the steps.

1. How many bats?

Cross out 4.
How many are left?

3. How many bats?

Cross out 4.
How many are left?

_ _ _

_____

2. How many bats?

Cross out 5.
How many are left?

_ _ _

_____

4. How many bats?

Cross out 5.
How many are left?

_ _ _

_____

How do you know how many are left?

Count the Syllables

Directions: Say the name of each picture. Write the number of syllables in each word.

 **Tip**

A *syllable* is a single speech sound. A syllable usually includes a vowel.

Example:  *pen-cil*

The word *pencil* has two syllables.

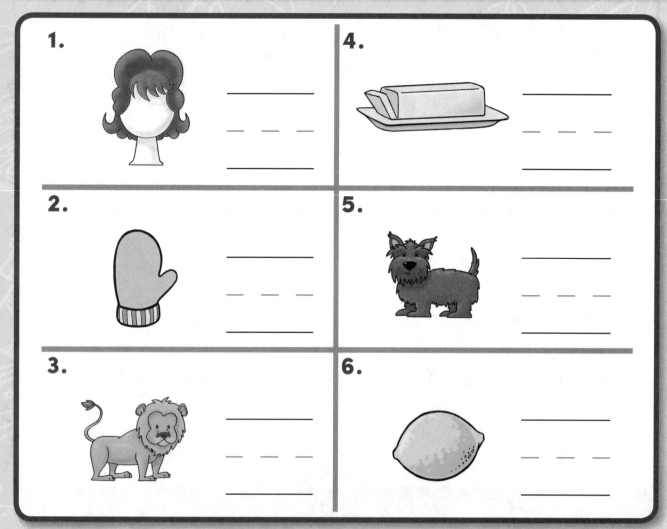

1.

2.

3.

4.

5.

6.

Talk About It!

How many syllables are in your name?

Add It Up

Directions: Count the items in each box. Write the sums.

1. $2 + 2 = 4$

2. ___ + ___ = ___

3. ___ + ___ = ___

4. ___ + ___ = ___

Talk About It!

How do you know how many there are in all?

Pal the Dog

Directions: Read the story with an adult. Then, answer the questions.

Pal is a dog. Pal can open the door. He can get Tim's shoes. He helps Tim a lot. He is a good friend.

1. What kind of animal is Pal?

   _____

   _____

2. What does Pal open?

   _____

   _____

3. What does Pal get?

   _____

   _____

4. Why is Pal a good friend?

   _____

   _____

Talk About It! Where in the story did you find the answer to each question?

Counting Caterpillars

Directions: Write the missing numbers.

Talk About It! How does the number line help you fill in the missing numbers on the caterpillar?

#17788—Kids Learn! Getting Ready for 1st Grade

Favorite Book

Directions: Draw and write about a book you like.

#17788—Kids Learn! Getting Ready for 1st Grade

Change the Letter

Directions: Change the first letter to make a new word to match each picture.

1. 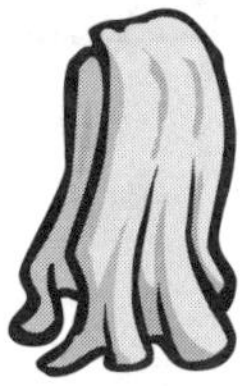 rag

bag

2.  cat

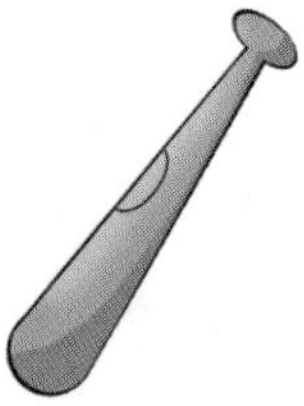

3.  dig

4.  dog

5.  luck

Talk About It!

Which letters stay the same in each word?

Add Some Eggs

Directions: Draw more eggs. Then, solve each problem.

1. Draw 2 more eggs.   Solve.

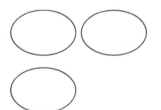 +   =

_____   +   _ _ _ _   =   _ _ _ _

2. Draw 3 more eggs.   Solve.

 +   =

_____   +   _ _ _ _   =   _ _ _ _

Talk About It!

How did you know which numbers to write in each number sentence?

Short O Words

Directions: Write the missing letters in the boxes to make words that name each picture.

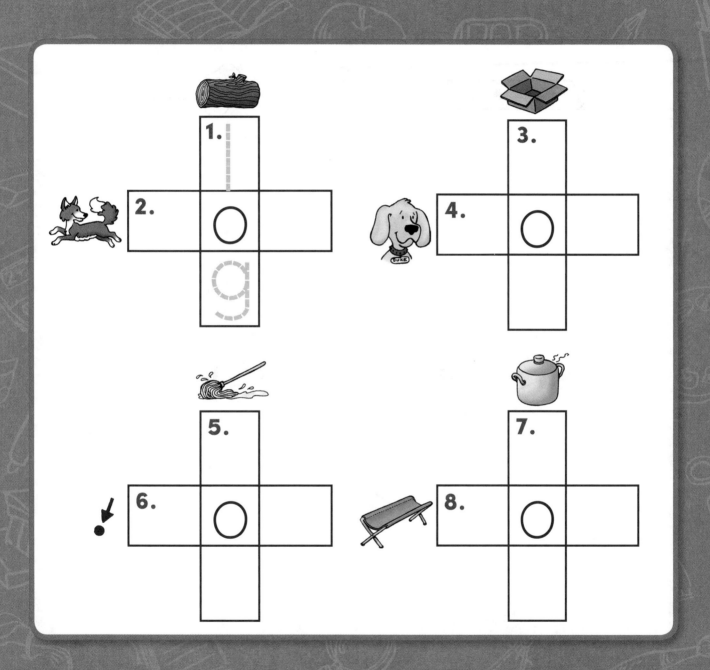

Talk About It! Find two words that rhyme on the page.

Make It Longer

Directions: Look at each object below. Draw a longer object.

1.

3.

2.

4.

Talk About It!

Which is the shortest object?

Read Tricky Words

Directions: Choose a word from the Word Bank to complete each sentence.

Word Bank

are	have	I	like

_____

1. I _____ a hen.

_____

2. _____ am a boy.

_____

3. I _____ my cat.

_____

4. They _____ kids.

Talk About It!

What other words could be used to fill in the blanks?

Subtract It!

Directions: Write number sentences to match the pictures.

1.

$$9 \quad - \quad 4 \quad = \quad 5$$

2.

_____ - _____ = _____

3.

_____ - _____ = _____

4.

_____ - _____ = _____

What does each number in the number sentence stand for?

#17788—Kids Learn! Getting Ready for 1st Grade

Choose the Vowel

Directions: Say the name of each picture. Circle the letter that matches the vowel sound.

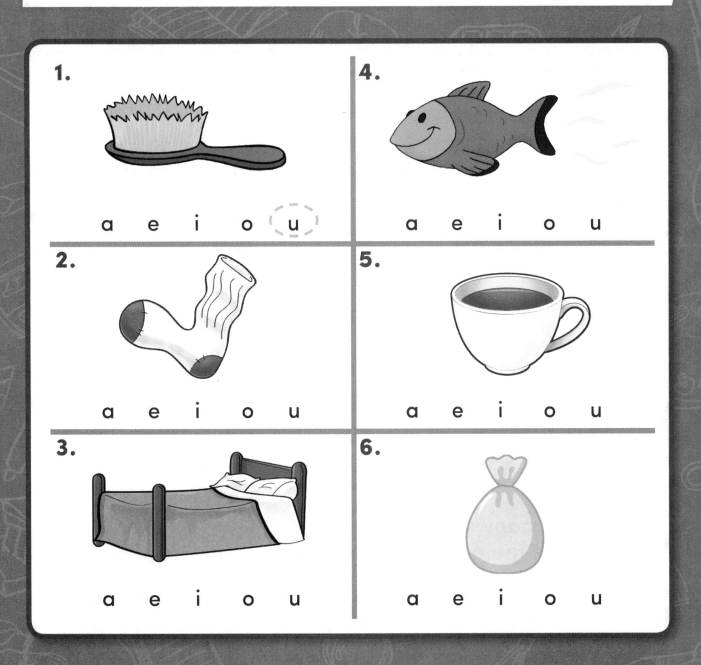

1.

a e i o (u)

2.

a e i o u

3.

a e i o u

4.

a e i o u

5.

a e i o u

6.

a e i o u

Talk About It!

Which vowels are in your name?

Count the Socks and Shoes

Directions: Count the socks and shoes. Then, compare them.

1. How many socks?  _5_
   Circle the group that shows *less* than the socks.

2. How many socks?  _____
   Circle the group that shows *more* than the socks.

3.  _____

   How many socks? _____
   Circle the group that shows *less* than the socks.

Talk About It!

What does the word *less* mean?

Short Vowels

Directions: Read each sentence. Write *yes* if it can be true. Write *no* if it cannot be true.

1. I can sip from a cup.   yes

2. A fish has a fin.   _____

3. A bell can run.   _____

4. A pig can play in the mud.   _____

5. He is six. Next, he will be ten.   _____

6. A fox can live in a den.   _____

Talk About It!

Say a sentence that is true and a sentence that is not true.

How Many?

Directions: Draw pictures to show how many.

1. Draw 12

3. Draw 13

2. Draw 15

4. Draw 14

Talk About It!

How many tens are in each problem?

Favorite Holiday

Directions: Draw and write about your favorite holiday.

Which Word?

Directions: Circle the word that completes the sentence.

1. Dan is in the _____.

   tan   van   ran

2. A baby is with his _____.

   dad   mad   sad

3. This is a _____ for Dan.

   tap   nap   cap

4. There is a _____ on the bag. →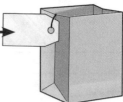

   tag   sat   cab

 **Talk About It!**

Which vowel was in all the word choices?

Plane or Solid Figures

Directions: Write *solid* under the solid figures. Write *plane* under the plane (flat) figures.

These are *plane* figures:

triangle   square

rectangle   circle

These are *solid* figures:

cube   prism

sphere   cone

1. _____ solid

2. _____

3. _____

4. _____

Talk About It! How do you know if an object is plane or solid?

Spell the Word

Directions: Say the name of each picture. Write the word.

1.

tub

2.

3.

4.

5.

6.

Talk About It!

How many letters are in each word?

Subtracting on a Number Line

Directions: Use the number line to show subtraction.

1. 5 – 3 =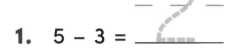

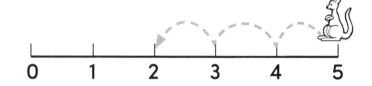

2. 4 – 1 = _____

3. 5 – 2 = _____

4. 3 – 1 = _____

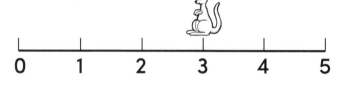

5. 4 – 2 = _____

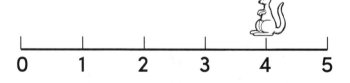

Talk About It!

Did you count forward or backward on the number line? Why?

Complete the Sentence

Directions: Say the name of each picture. Write the word on the line.

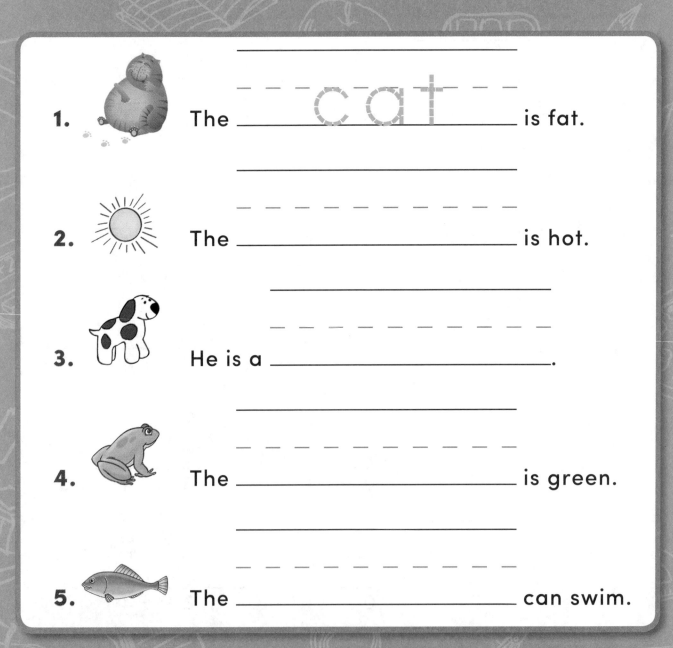

1. The ____ cat ____ is fat.

2. The _____ is hot.

3. He is a _____.

4. The _____ is green.

5. The _____ can swim.

Talk About It!

How did you figure out how to spell each word?

Adding Animals

Directions: Read the word problems. Count the animals to find the sum.

1. I see 4 monkeys. I see 5 lions.
   How many animals in all?

   4 + 5 = _____ animals

2. I see 2 bears. I see 6 zebras.
   How many animals in all?

   _____

   _ _ _

   2 + 6 = _____ animals

3. I see 7 dogs. I see 3 cats.
   How many animals in all?

   _____

   _ _ _

   7 + 3 = _____ animals

Talk About It!

How did you find the sums?

Short O Rhymes

Directions: Find the socks with words that rhyme. Draw lines to connect the pairs.

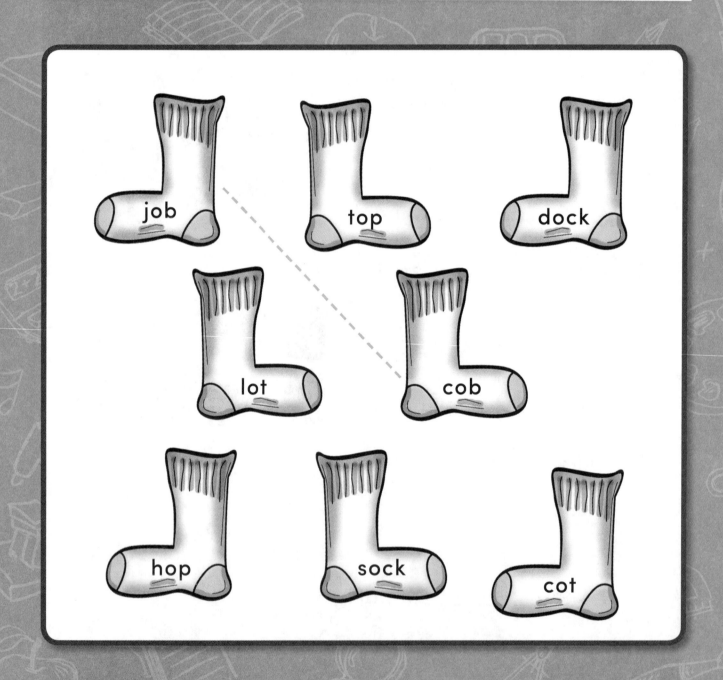

job   top   dock

lot   cob

hop   sock   cot

Talk About It! Say another word that rhymes with each pair of rhyming words.

#17788—Kids Learn! Getting Ready for 1st Grade

Comparing Numbers

Directions: Look at the numbers in the boxes. Draw a circle around the number that has less. Cross out the number that has more.

1. 10   9

2. 9   8

3. 7   8

4. 11   10

more

less

Talk About It!

What is a number that is more than the largest number on the page?

Sentence Completion

Directions: Write a word from the Word Bank to complete the sentence.

Word Bank

kiss   jet   pet   boss   bun

1. Ten men flew on the _____ jet _____.

2. I want to eat this _____.

3. I have a dog for a _____.

4. At the job he is the _____.

5. I gave my mom a _____.

Talk About It!

Which words from the Word Bank begin with the same sound?

Writing Numbers to 30

Directions: Write the missing numbers.

1	2	3
	5	
10		
	14	
		18
		21
	26	

Talk About It! How do you know which number comes next?

Playground Fun

Directions: Draw and write about something you do on the playground.

Change a Letter

Directions: Start with the word written in the car. Change the letters to make new words.

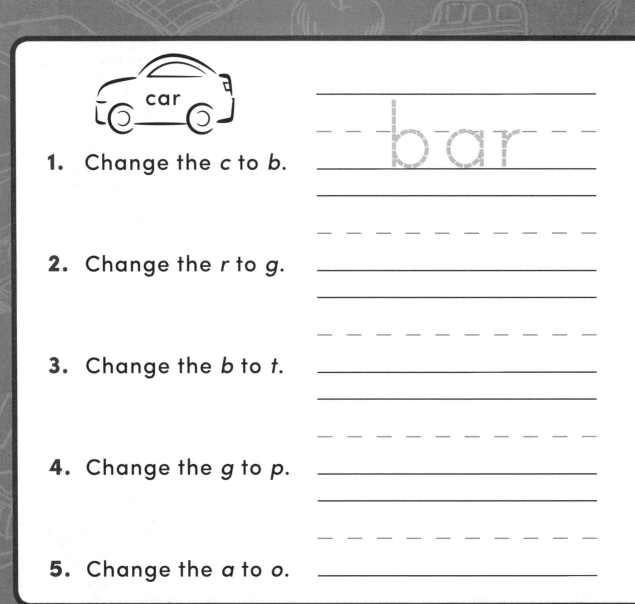

car

1. Change the *c* to *b*.   bar

2. Change the *r* to *g*.

3. Change the *b* to *t*.

4. Change the *g* to *p*.

5. Change the *a* to *o*.

Talk About It!

Read each new word you wrote.

Identifying Shapes

Directions: Draw a line from each clue to the answer.

1. I have no points.
   I have no straight lines.
   I am round. What am I?

2. I have straight sides.
   I have three corners.
   What am I?

3. I have four sides.
   I have four corners.
   I look like a box.
   What am I?

4. I have four sides.
   My sides are straight.
   I am not a square.
   What am I?

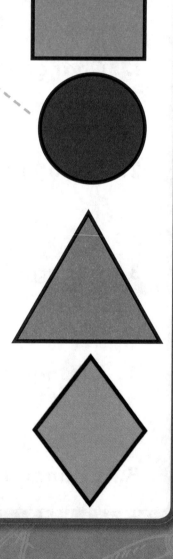

Name three objects that are a circle.

#17788—Kids Learn! Getting Ready for 1st Grade

Complete the Word

Directions: Say the name of each picture. Write the letters for the beginning and ending sounds.

1.

g u m

2.

a

3.

i

4.

o

5.

e

6.

i

Talk About It!

How many sounds does each word have?

Size It Up

Directions: Circle the smaller object in each box.

1.

3.

2.

4.

Talk About It!

Which is the smallest object on the page?

Find the Right Word

Directions: Choose a word from the Word Bank to complete each sentence.

Word Bank

Do   with   is   have

1. _____ you like apples?

2. I _____ a ball.

3. The bed _____ big.

4. He is _____ the girl.

Why is the word *do* capitalized?

Adding Outdoors

Directions: Add to find the answers to each word problem.

1. I see 5 girls. I see 2 boys. How many in all?

    5 + 2 = _____

2. I see 3 clouds. I see 1 sun. How many in all?

    3 + 1 = _____

3. I see 2 swings. I see 2 jump ropes. How many in all?

    2 + 2 = _____

Make up your own addition story problem.

Rhyme Time

Directions: Say the name of the picture in the box. Circle the picture that rhymes.

Talk About It! Which part of rhyming words sounds the same?

Count the Beach Balls

Directions: Answer the questions.

1.

Draw one more.

How many? ___14___

2.

Draw one more.

How many? _____

3.

Draw one more.

How many? _____

Talk About It! Does a number get larger or smaller when you add one more? How do you know?

Ducks

Directions: Read the text. Then, answer the questions.

A mother duck is called a hen. She makes a nest. She may lay eggs. The babies hatch in four weeks. The babies are called ducklings.

1. What is a mother duck called?

   _____

   _____

2. What does a hen make?

   _____

   _____

3. How many weeks does it take for the babies to hatch?

   _____

   _____

4. What are the babies called?

   _____

   _____

 **Talk About It!**

Which sentence in the story helped you answer question 3?

How Many Balloons?

Directions: Count the balloons. Write the number.

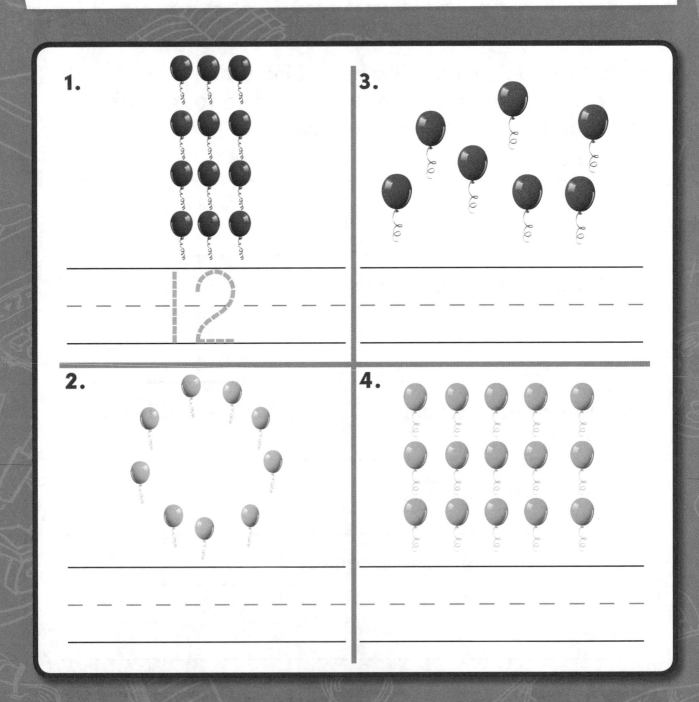

1. _____

12

2. _____

3. _____

4. _____

Talk About It!

Which group has the most balloons? How do you know?

Favorite Food

Directions: Draw and write about your favorite food. Use your five senses to help you describe it.

Great Work!

_____

(Name)

has completed

Kids Learn! Getting Ready for 1st Grade

_____

(Date)

Extra Activities

© Teacher Created Materials

#17788—Kids Learn! Getting Ready for 1st Grade

83

Be Observant

Directions: Get a piece of fruit. Observe it with your five senses. Write or draw about what you find.

see

_____

hear

_____

touch

_____

smell

_____

taste

Flip It

Directions: Cut out the letters. Put them facedown. Turn two letters over and place them in the boxes below. Read the word. If it makes a real word, write the word on the lines below. If not, try again. Make as many words as you can.

i

p
n
g
t
l
d

Hundreds Chart

Directions: Fill in the missing numbers on the chart.

0	1	2			5				9
10			13				17		
20	21			24				28	
30		32			35				39
40			43			46			
50	51						57		
60				64				68	
70		72				76			
80			83						89
90					95				
100									

Rules for Crossing the Street

Directions: Read the text with a parent.

Do you like to take walks? What do you do when you want to cross the street? You need to be safe. Here are some rules.

1. Do not cross in the middle of the street.

2. Always cross at the corner crosswalks.

3. At lights, look for the "walk" sign. Cross when the sign says "walk."

4. Always look both ways first.

5. Cross the street quickly. But, be safe, too.

 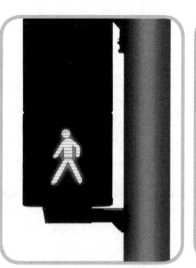 

Rules for Crossing the Street (cont.)

Directions: Write *1*, *2*, or *3* next to the sentences to put them in logical order. Then, read the paragraph and underline the sentence that does not belong.

_____ Cross the street as fast as you can.

_____ Look both ways.

_____ At lights, cross only when the sign says "walk."

I crossed the street at the crosswalk. I like to run and walk fast. First, I looked both ways. Then, I walked across the street.

National Symbols

Directions: Read the text. Then, answer the questions.

The United States has many symbols. The flag has 13 stripes and 50 stars. The Statue of Liberty and the Liberty Bell are symbols of freedom. The bald eagle is a strong bird. It is a symbol of strength.

1. Which is a symbol of strength?

   (A) the flag

   (B) the Liberty Bell

   (C) the bald eagle

2. How many stripes are on the flag?

   (A) 13

   (B) 50

   (C) 10

3. Which is *not* a symbol of freedom?

   (A) stars

   (B) the Liberty Bell

   (C) the Statue of Liberty

4. What country are these symbols for?

   (A) Canada

   (B) France

   (C) the United States

Make Shapes

Directions: Follow the steps to make new shapes.

1. Cut out the shapes at the bottom.
2. Arrange two shapes to make a rectangle.
3. Arrange three shapes to make a trapezoid.
4. Arrange three shapes to make a square.

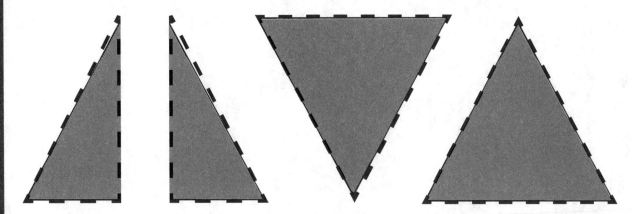

Make New Words

Directions: Choose a beginning letter from the first circle. Then, choose a word ending from the second circle. Write the word on the line. Circle the word if it is not a real word. Make as many words as you can.

c b
h t

-ut -ug
-un -ub

cut

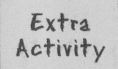

Frogs on a Log

Directions: Read the text with a parent.

See the frogs.

They live in a lake.

Frogs sit on logs.

They like the sun.

It helps them get warm.

94

#17788—*Kids Learn! Getting Ready for 1st Grade*

© *Teacher Created Materials*

Frogs on a Log (cont.)

Directions: Read the problem below. Follow the steps to solve the problem.

Read

There are 6 frogs on the log. Then 2 more frogs hop onto the log. How many frogs are on the log now?

Think

What do I know?
Write or draw.

What do I need to find out? Write or draw.

Solve

This is my answer. Write or draw.

Reflect

Does my answer make sense? Circle one.

yes   no

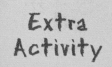

Create a Scene

Directions: Choose a character and circle it. Choose a setting and circle it. Draw a picture that shows the character in the setting you chose.

Characters		Settings	
Dog	Clown	Park	Forest
Cat	Firefighter	Beach	Bedroom
Girl	Pig	School	Farm
Boy	Teacher	House	Pizza Shop

Writing Paper

Writing Paper

Writing Paper

Writing Paper

Writing Paper

Writing Paper

Writing Paper

Writing Paper

Answer Key

Page 14

1. bun
2. run
3. fun
4. man
5. ran
6. can

Talk About It: The first letter changes in each word.

Page 15

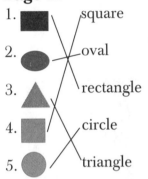

1. square
2. oval
3. rectangle
4. circle
5. triangle

Talk About It: A square is a special kind of rectangle with four equal sides.

Page 16

1. b
2. d
3. h
4. r
5. n
6. n

Talk About It: Children should give the sounds of the letters above.

Page 17

The following pictures should be circled:

1.
2.
3.
4.
5.
6.

Talk About It: The elephant is the heaviest.

Page 18

Talk About It: Possible answer: I said the alphabet in order to know which letter came next.

Page 19

1. $4 + 4 = 8$
2. $3 + 3 = 6$
3. $1 + 4 = 5$

Talk About It: The total is larger because you get more when you add things together.

Page 20

1. A
2. B
3. C
4. C
5. A
6. A

Talk About It: Answers will vary.

Page 21

1. 9, 10, 11, 12, 13
2. 14, 15, 16, 17, 18
3. 7, 8, 9, 10, 11
4. 16, 17, 18, 19, 20
5. 12, 13, 14, 15, 16
6. 3, 4, 5, 6, 7

Talk About It: The largest number is 20. All other numbers are less than 20.

Page 22

1. hand
2. fin
3. bed
4. duck
5. bat
6. hen

Talk About It: Answers will vary.

Page 23

1. 4
2. 11
3. 7
4. 13

Talk About It: The numbers got larger because another watermelon was added to each group.

Page 24

Answers will vary.

Page 25

1. t
2. t
3. t
4. n
5. n
6. n

Talk About It: Answers will vary.

Page 26

1. s
2. p
3. p
4. p
5. s
6. p

Talk About It: Answers will vary. Possible answers: ball, planet, sun, moon, etc.

Answer Key (cont.)

Page 27

1. was
2. for
3. not
4. that

Page 28

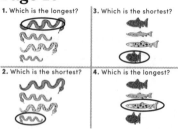

1. Which is the longest?

3. Which is the shortest?

2. Which is the shortest?

4. Which is the longest?

Talk About It: The longest animal is the pink snake. The shortest animal is the blue fish

Page 29

1. I have a dog. □
   i have a dog. ☑
2. My dog has spots. □
   my dog has spots. ☑
3. May i pet your dog? ☑
   May I pet your dog? □
4. your dog is big! ☑
   Your dog is big! □

Talk About It: The first word always begins with a capital letter.

Page 30

1. 1
2. 2
3. 3
4. 1
5. 2
6. 5

Talk About It: Answers will vary. Possible answer: I knew how many were left by counting the ones that weren't crossed out.

Page 31

1.

2.

3.

4.

Talk About It: Answers will vary. Possible answers: took, look, crook, etc.

Page 32

1. X on 2; circle 3
2. X on 0; circle 8
3. X on 7; circle 8
4. X on 5; circle 6

Talk About It: 8

Page 33

1. The pig is in the pen.
2. The frog is on the lily pad.
3. The bug is in the net.
4. The dog ran in the sun.

Talk About It: The word that is different is *sat/ran.*

Page 34

1. 10
2. 9
3. 6
4. 8

Talk About It: Problem 4 shows 4 pairs of shoes.

Page 35

Answers will vary.

Page 36

Answers will vary. Possible answers:

1. cab; lab, jab
2. sad; bad, mad
3. pan; tan, man
4. cat; bat, mat

Talk About It: The first letter was changed to make rhyming words.

Page 37

Talk About It: A rectangle has 4 sides and its opposite sides are the same length.

Page 38

1. pig
2. six
3. swim
4. bib
5. pin
6. lip

Talk About It: The vowel *i* is in each word.

Page 39

Talk About It: Answers will vary.

#17788—Kids Learn! Getting Ready for 1st Grade

Answer Key (cont.)

Page 40

1. pig
2. pans
3. hats
4. sun

Talk About It: The letter *s* added to the end of a word shows more than one.

Page 41

1. 7; 3
2. 9; 4
3. 8; 4
4. 6; 1

Talk About It: Possible answer: I counted the items that are left after crossing out to know how many were left.

Page 42

1. 1
2. 2
3. 2
4. 2
5. 1
6. 2

Talk About It: Answers will vary.

Page 43

1. $2 + 2 = 4$
2. $3 + 3 = 6$
3. $0 + 6 = 6$
4. $4 + 6 = 10$

Talk About It: Possible answer: I counted all of the things to know how many there are in all.

Page 44

1. A dog
2. The door
3. Tim's shoes
4. He helps Tim.

Talk About It: Child should show where he or she found the answers.

Page 45

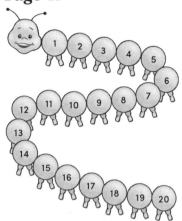

Talk About It: Possible answer: The number line shows the numbers that come before and after the missing number.

Page 46

Answers will vary.

Page 47

1. bag
2. bat
3. pig
4. log
5. duck

Talk About It: All the letters stay the same except for the first letter.

Page 48

1. $4 + 2 = 6$
2. $3 + 3 = 6$

Talk About It: Possible answer: I counted each group of eggs, and then I counted all the eggs to find the total.

Page 49

1. log
2. fox
3. box
4. dog
5. mop
6. dot
7. pot
8. cot

Talk About It: Possible answers: log and dog; pot and cot; fox and box

Page 50

Answers will vary.

Page 51

1. have
2. I
3. like
4. are

Talk About It: Answers will vary.

Page 52

1. $9 - 4 = 5$
2. $8 - 3 = 5$
3. $7 - 5 = 2$
4. $8 - 4 = 4$

Talk About It: Answers will vary. Children should explain what each number represents in each number sentence.

Page 53

1. u
2. o
3. e
4. i
5. u
6. a

Talk About It: Answers will vary.

Answer Key (cont.)

Page 54

1. 5; 👟👟👟👟👟
2. 6; 👟👟👟👟👟👟👟
3. 7; 👟👟👟👟👟👟

Talk About It: Less means not as many.

Page 55

1. yes
2. yes
3. no
4. yes
5. no
6. yes

Talk About It: Answers will vary.

Page 56

1. Picture should show 12 balls.
2. Picture should show 15 stars.
3. Picture should show 13 hearts.
4. Picture should show 14 diamonds.

Talk About It: There is one ten in each problem.

Page 57

Answers will vary.

Page 58

1. van
2. dad
3. cap
4. tag

Talk About It: The vowel *a* was in all the word choices.

Page 59

1. solid
2. solid
3. plane
4. plane

Talk About It: Possible answer: Solid objects have many faces and can be held in your hand.

Page 60

1. tub
2. cut
3. bus
4. hut
5. sun
6. sub

Talk About It: There are three letters in each word.

Page 61

1. 2;
2. 3;
3. 3;
4. 2;
5. 2;

Talk About It: Possible answer: I counted backward on the number line because I took away.

Page 62

1. cat
2. sun
3. dog
4. frog
5. fish

Talk About It: Possible answer: I sounded out the letters in each word.

Page 63

1. 9
2. 8
3. 10

Talk About It: Possible answer: I counted all of the animals together.

Page 64

job, cob

top, hop

dock, sock

lot, cot

Talk About It: Answers will vary. Possible answers: sob; shop; tock; dot

Page 65

1. X on 10; circle 9
2. X on 9; circle 8
3. X on 8; circle 7
4. X on 11; circle 10

Talk About It: Answers will vary, but should be larger than 11.

Page 66

1. jet
2. bun
3. pet
4. boss
5. kiss

Talk About It: boss and *bun* begin with the same sound.

Answer Key (cont.)

Page 67

1	2	3
4	5	6
7	8	9
10	11	12
13	14	15
16	17	18
19	20	21
22	23	24
25	26	27
28	29	30

Talk About It: By counting in order, I know which number comes next.

Page 68

Answers will vary.

Page 69

1. bar
2. bag
3. tag
4. tap
5. top

Page 70

1.
2.
3.
4.

Talk About It: Answers will vary. Possible answers: plate, coin, button, etc.

Page 71

1. gum
2. bat
3. six
4. mop
5. ten
6. wig

Talk About It: Each word has three sounds.

Page 72

1.
2.
3.
4.

Talk About It: The strawberry is the smallest object on the page.

Page 73

1. Do
2. have
3. is
4. with

Talk About It: Do is capitalized because it is the first word in the question.

Page 74

1. 7
2. 4
3. 4

Talk About It: Answers will vary.

Page 75

1.
2.
3.
4.

Talk About It: The end of rhyming words sounds the same.

Page 76

1. 14
2. 12
3. 16

Talk About It: A number gets larger when you add one more. There are more things, so the number is bigger.

Page 77

1. a hen
2. a nest
3. four weeks
4. ducklings

Talk About It: The fourth sentence.

Page 78

1. 12
2. 9
3. 7
4. 15

Talk About It: Possible answer: The group of green balloons has the most. I counted, and 15 is more than any other group.

Page 79

Answers will vary.

Page 84

Answers will vary.

Page 85

Answers will vary. Possible answers: pin, tin, nip, dip, dig, tip, lid, lip, lit.

Answer Key *(cont.)*

Page 87

0	1	2	3	4	5	6	7	8	9
10	11	12	13	14	15	16	17	18	19
20	21	22	23	24	25	26	27	28	29
30	31	32	33	34	35	36	37	38	39
40	41	42	43	44	45	46	47	48	49
50	51	52	53	54	55	56	57	58	59
60	61	62	63	64	65	66	67	68	69
70	71	72	73	74	75	76	77	78	79
80	81	82	83	84	85	86	87	88	89
90	91	92	93	94	95	96	97	98	99
100									

Page 89

3; 2; 1; I like to run and walk fast.

Page 90

1. C

2. A

3. A

4. C

Page 91

2.

3.

4.

Page 93

Answers will vary. Possible answers: cut, cug, cun, cub, but, bug, bun, bub, hut, hug, hun, hub, tut, tug, tun, tub. Insert circles around cug, cun, bub, hun, tun, tut.

Page 95

Answers will vary. Possible answers include drawings or number sentences to show $6 + 2 = 8$.

Page 96

Answers will vary.

Kids Learn! Parent Survey

Dear Parent,

The activities in this *Kids Learn!* book have helped your child review grade-level skills from the recent school year and get ready for the year ahead. Your feedback on this learning resource is very valuable. Please complete the survey below and return it as directed by your child's teacher or school administrator. Thank you in advance for your input and your time.

Please circle the term that best describes how you feel about this *Kids Learn!* book.

1. The **Introduction** (pages 4–12) gave me good ideas for things to do with my child and offered helpful resources for extended learning.

   Strongly Agree   Agree   Disagree   Strongly Disagree

   Comments: _____

   _____

2. The **Weekly Activities for Students** (pages 14–79) were easy to understand and helped me guide my child to complete the activity sheets. The activities were at an appropriate level of difficulty for my child.

   Strongly Agree   Agree   Disagree   Strongly Disagree

   Comments: _____

   _____

3. The sections of *Kids Learn!* that were particularly helpful or useful for me and my child were: (*Please check all that apply.*)

   ☐ Top 10 Things Your First Grader Will Need to Know

   ☐ Websites and Apps for Parents and Kids

   ☐ Things to Do at Home

   ☐ Weekly Activities for Students

   ☐ Things to Do in the Community

   ☐ Extra Activities

   ☐ Suggested Vacation Reading and Log

Please provide any additional comments or suggestions about this *Kids Learn!* book.

_____

_____

_____